Goose berry Patch Co. ®

Sleigh Bells & Mistletoe
A Christmas Journal

This Christmas Journal Belongs to:

_____

_____

A Country Store In Your Mailbox®

Gooseberry Patch
149 Johnson Drive
Department BOOK
Delaware, OH 43015
★
1·800·85·GOOSE
1-800·854·6673

Copyright 1995, **Gooseberry Patch** 0-9632978-6-4
Second Printing, October, 1998

How To Subscribe

Would you like to receive
"A Country Store in Your Mailbox®?"
For a 2-year subscription to our 88-page
Gooseberry Patch catalog, simply send $3.00 to:

Gooseberry Patch
149 Johnson Drive
Department BOOK
Delaware, OH 43015

CONTENTS

My Christmas Memories

Decorate under your tree with old toys... a train,

dy, or doll. What wonderful memories this will bring back.

A nice way to spend Christmas Eve is to have each family member...

share a favorite memory of times past, read a
short story or poem, or sing
a Christmas song.

PLANNING AN
OLD-FASHIONED
Country Christmas

_____

_____

_____

_____

_____

_____

_____

_____

_____

_____

_____

_____

_____

"Over the river and through
the wood,
To grandmother's house we go;
The horse knows the way
To carry the sleigh,
through the white and drifted
snow.

Over the river and through
the wood,
Oh how the wind does blow;
It stings the toes
And bites the nose,
As over the ground we go."
Lydia Maria Child

countdown to Christmas

_____

_____

_____

_____

_____

_____

_____

_____

_____

_____

Before the big day, don't
forget to stock up on
film, batteries, candles,
videotapes, and a gift or
two for unexpected guests.

Pamper yourself a bit during the holidays.

_____
_____
_____
_____
_____
_____
_____
_____
_____
_____
_____
_____
_____
_____
_____
_____
_____
_____
_____

Treat yourself to a massage, manicure, facial, or bubble bath; hire a housekeeper for

day; enjoy a cup of hot cider by the fire; or take a long drive and enjoy the Christmas lights.

13

EASY HOLIDAY How-To's

_____

_____

_____

_____

_____

_____

_____

_____

_____

_____

_____

_____

_____

•RECIPE FOR "CHRISTMAS FRAGRANCE":
Simmer cinnamon sticks, lemon and orange peel, cloves, and nutmeg. Instantly, your home will have the warm, cozy fragrance of the holidays!

·CINNAMON ORNAMENTS·

Hang these fragrant cut-outs on your tree, tie them on packages, or scent your potpourri! Just mix 1 ½ cups cinnamon and 1 cup smooth applesauce. Should be dough consistency. Roll out on wax paper and cut out tiny cookie cutter shapes. Make a hole for hanging with a straw. Let dry for several days.

· POMANDERS·

Using a toothpick, punch tiny holes in your orange and push a whole clove in each hole. Roll orange in cinnamon and orris root mixture (1 T. each) and let cure about 4 weeks. They smell wonderful!

· CHRISTMAS WRAP, TAGS, & RECIPE CARDS ·

Create your own gift wrap, tags, and recipe cards with rubber stamps. All you'll need is brown Kraft paper, white shelf paper, plain index cards, a variety of rubber stamps, inkpads, markers, and a little imagination! For extra sparkle, a gold felt-tip pen is nice for writing on names, sprinkling stars, and adding borders.

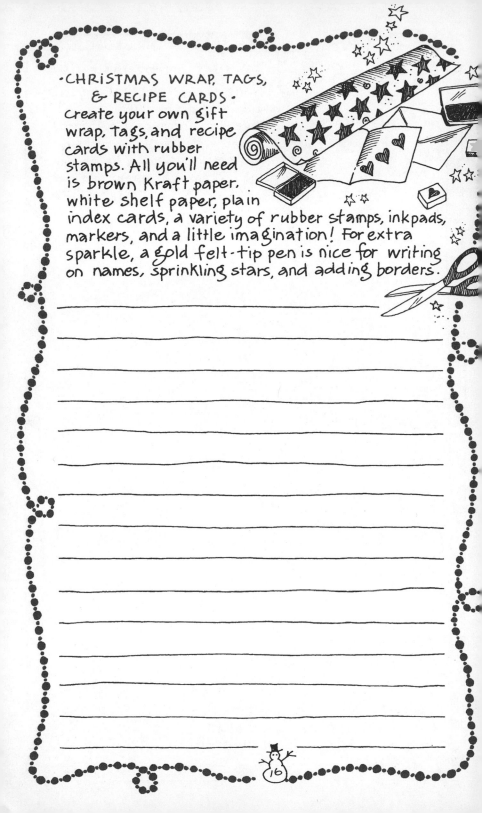

· YULETIDE POTPOURRI ·

2 c. pine needles	dried orange peel
1 c. bay leaves	cinnamon sticks
3 T. rosemary	tiny pine cones
1 T. whole cloves	berries
2 T. ground orris root	14 drops cinnamon oil

Mix dry ingredients in a ceramic or glass bowl. In a separate container, stir together the ground orris root and cinnamon oil. Add this to the dried mixture. Toss gently. Allow to cure for 2 weeks in a tightly closed container in a cool, dark place. Shake occasionally.

CHRISTMAS NOTES

Hot glue "naturals" onto your holiday packages...pomegranates, greenery...

18

sticks, herbs, or bay leaves. You'll hear lots of ooh's and ahh's!

erries, acorn, moss, dried oranges, apples, cinnamon

19

HOLIDAY GIFT IDEAS

Wrap up a
pretty pillow, good book,
packet of herbal tea with
a big bow and a wish for
"Sweet Christmas Dreams."

Give the gift of time all year long. Volunteer at local food banks and homeless shelters; make food baskets for the elderly; donate clothes for the less fortunate; visit nursing homes; and collect toys for needy children.

Gift Basket Fillers
&
STOCKING STUFFER
Ideas

pot pourris • candles • homemade ornaments •
cookie cutters • tiny boxed candies • teas,
coffees, cocoas • cups • spices • kitchen gadgets •
homespun towels • seeds • soaps • gourmet jams
and jellies • calendars • journals • recipe books •
recipe cards • note cards • gift certificates •
cassettes, CD's • magazine subscriptions •
• homemade coupons •

CHRISTMAS COLLECTIONS

- santas
- angels • snowmen
- cookie cutters
- Christmas books & cookbooks
- gingerbread men • teddy bears
- trees • stars • gnomes
- Noah's arks • ornaments
- candles • stockings
- villages

_____

_____

_____

_____

_____

_____

christmas Shopping List

Decorate your mantel
with freshly cut pine,
holly, evergreen,
mistletoe, and juniper.
Tuck in apples, pine cones,
twigs, and berries...
simply beautiful!

Bundle up several candles and tie with a French wire ribbon bow...

Beautiful!

Handy

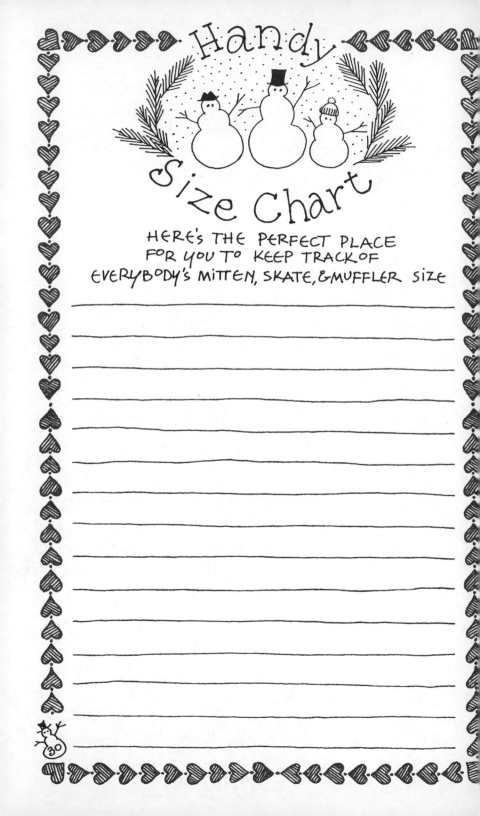

Size Chart

HERE'S THE PERFECT PLACE
FOR YOU TO KEEP TRACK OF
EVERYBODY'S MITTEN, SKATE, & MUFFLER SIZE

_____
_____
_____
_____
_____
_____
_____
_____
_____
_____
_____
_____
_____
_____
_____

"Christmas is coming, the geese are getting fat..."

UNKNOWN

my CHristMas WiSH List

_____

_____

_____

_____

_____

_____

_____

_____

_____

_____

_____

_____

_____

_____

_____

Catch a snowflake on the tip of your tongue on

LET IT SNOW

Christmas Eve and good luck will be yours for the coming year.

33

Decking the Halls

Ideas for Decorating Doors · Windows · Trees · the Dog... (don't forget the Car... & the Cat)

Bring out all your

very best quilts and layer in chairs, couches;
fold on top of cupboards... make
your home cozy for the holidays.

When stringing pomegranates, cinnamon sticks, pine cones, and acorns for garlands, use a small drill. It makes it so much easier!

Joyful traditions

_____

_____

_____

_____

_____

_____

_____

_____

_____

_____

_____

_____

_____

_____

_____

_____

_____

_____

Take time out during the busy holiday season

go out to dinner with someone special or have a winter picnic by the fire.

Animals have
Christmas traditions all their
own. So the legend goes,
for one hour on Christmas Eve,
all animals can speak.

_____

_____

_____

_____

_____

_____

_____

_____

_____

_____

_____

Holiday Brainstorming

Believe in Santa with all your might and your dreams will come true.

·f·e·s·t·i·v·e·
PARTY THEMES
celebrate the season!

COOKIE EXCHANGE: Invite a dozen friends over. Ask them each to bring 3 dozen cookies packaged in 3's. Each guest will go home with 3 dozen cookies (12 different kinds). Share recipes and have a good time.

HOLIDAY DESSERT PARTY: Invite your friends for 8:00 and serve several different desserts with coffee, brandy, and dessert wines. Fruit and cheese are nice accompaniments.

HANDMADE ORNAMENT EXCHANGE: Invite a dozen friends over and ask each one to bring a dozen handmade ornaments. Each guest goes home with 12 new ornaments for their Christmas tree.

HOLIDAY OPEN HOUSE: A holiday open house is one of the most festive ways to celebrate the season with family and friends. Add music, hot spiced cider, Christmas cookies, candles, a crackling fire, and a little mistletoe!

POT POURRI GET-TOGETHER:
Each person brings one ingredient...pine cones, cinnamon sticks, lemon peels, orange peels, cloves, nutmegs, pomanders, berries, pine sprigs or cinnamon cut-outs. Mix with cinnamon oil, scoop cupfuls into cellophane bags, tie with pretty ribbons, and send samples home with each guest.

CHRISTMAS TEA or COFFEE PARTY:
Thermoses keep beverages hot (identify what each one has inside). For coffee lovers, offer little "extras" like chocolate or almond whipped cream, egg nog, chocolate milk, chocolate-coated espresso beans, chocolate mints, and even spoons dipped in chocolate for stirring! For those who prefer tea... red hots, cinnamon sticks, lemon slices, and candy canes are yummy. Don't forget to serve pound cake and cookies.

CHRISTMAS CAROLING:
Fill a van (or more than one) with plenty of warm blankets and lots of good friends. Open the windows, play Christmas carols and wish all a "Merry Christmas!" A tailgate party with hot cocoa and Christmas cookies would be a happy ending.

HOLIDAY BRUNCH:
Invite everyone over for a Saturday morning brunch – egg casserole, sizzling bacon, home fries, blueberry muffins, fresh fruit, juices, coffee. The secret? Simplicity!

TREE TRIMMING PARTY:
All you need is a tree, lots of ornaments, good food, good friends, and good fun!

holiday entertaining

Gilding adds holiday sparkle to dried fruit, cinnamon sticks, pinecones, leaves, artichokes, just about anything! Spray gold paint evenly and let dry. For extra glitter, add a gold French wire ribbon bow.

47

Surround your holiday punch bowl with greenery, berries, shiny red apples, gold pears, and spicy pomanders!

☆Party Planning CHECKLIST

beverages (beer, wine, soft drinks) _____

cheese _____

chips, pretzels _____

coffee _____

crackers _____

dip _____

fresh flowers _____

candles _____

fresh fruit

_____ fancy toothpicks

_____ hors d'oeuvres, platters (deli)

_____ ice

_____ lemons, limes, maraschino cherries

_____ mints

_____ mixers

plates, cups, napkins

nuts

pickles, olives

my favorite CHRiSTMAS recipes

yum yum
yum yum
yum yum yummy
yummy yum yum

when cookies co

mist with water
and decorate with
edible gold leaf.
So elegant!

Personalize holiday dessert plates. Pour thick chocolate syrup in a small zip lock bag. Cut tip off corner of bag and pipe guests' names onto their plates. Serve white chocolate cheesecake and listen to the raves!

· Freeze your cookies up to 3 months ahead ·

And you won't have to "cram" so much into the holidays.

Your holiday table will look beautiful with a big basket of red and green fruits and veggies.

Blow up a balloon, dip in chocolate, let set and pop... instant chocolate bowl for serving holiday goodies!

THE christmas PANTRY

Necessaries for Holiday Baking

baking chocolate
chocolate chips
milk, cream,
     evaporated milk
corn syrup
baking soda
baking powder
salt
raisins
walnuts, pecans
white sugar
brown sugar
powdered sugar
all-purpose flour
food colorings

molasses
cinnamon, allspice,
    nutmeg, cloves, ginger
sprinkles, jimmies,
    glittery sugars
shortening
vanilla
eggs
butter

TRIED & TRUE
HOLIDAY MENUS

_____

_____

_____

_____

_____

_____

_____

_____

_____

_____

_____

_____

_____

_____

_____

_____

It's
Christmas!
Get out your
favorite candle-
sticks...pewter, brass,
and silver. Buy lots of
white candles and
dress them up with golden
French wire ribbon bows,
foil stars, pine, and berries.

65

Sprinkle shiny gold stars... everywhere... on your tablecloth, on the packages under your tree and in side cards and letters, like pixie dust.

67

Everyone loves cookies at Christmas! Fill a basket, bowl, or X

68

h your favorite Christmas cookies and tuck in the recipe for a special surprise.

69

Holiday Tablesettings

Set a festive holiday table...fragrant greenery, golden ribbon, snowy white linens, candles, crystal, and shiny Christmas bulbs will make your table sparkle!

GIFTS
from my
COUNTRY
KITCHEN

_____
_____
_____
_____
_____
_____
_____
_____
_____
_____
_____
_____
_____
_____

Fill gift baskets with easy-to-make gifts of...

_____
_____
_____
_____
_____
_____
_____
_____
_____
_____
_____
_____
_____
_____
_____
_____

from your Christmas kitchen... spiced nuts, herbal vinegars, jams and jellies, homemade pickles, nut breads, and holiday cookies!

Bread

73

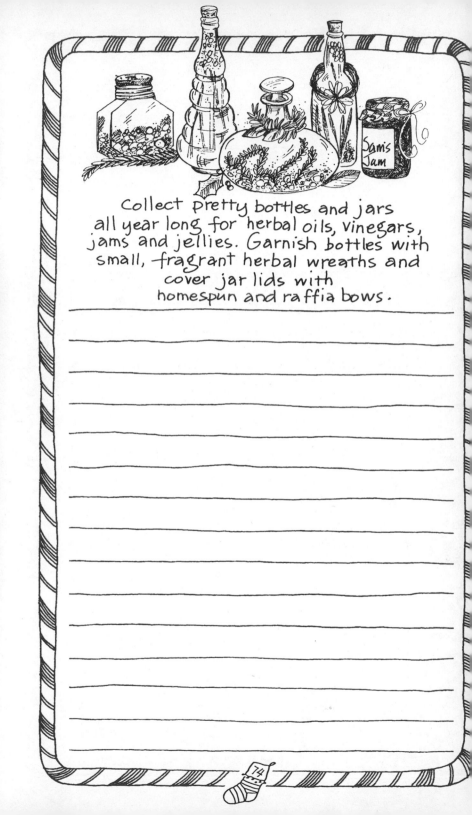

Collect pretty bottles and jars
all year long for herbal oils, vinegars,
jams and jellies. Garnish bottles with
small, fragrant herbal wreaths and
cover jar lids with
homespun and raffia bows.

A kitchen towel is the perfect "wrap" for a cookbook and don't forget to tie on a cookie cutter or wooden spoon.

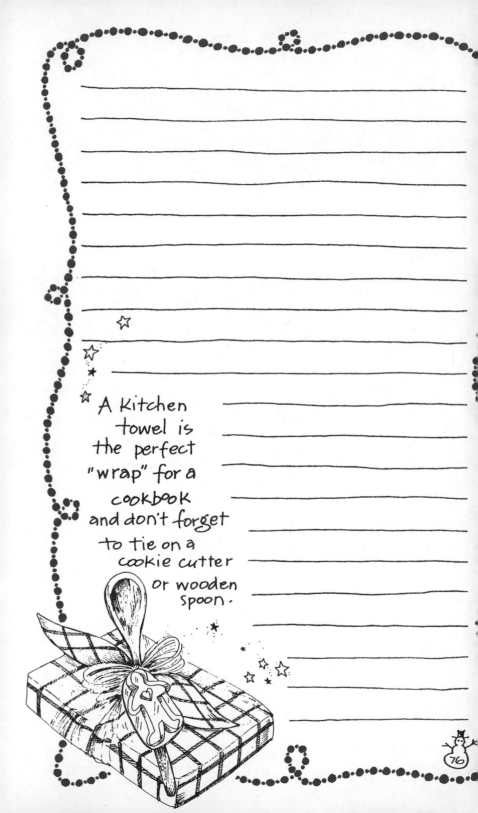

Carve out apples, oranges, and artichokes and tuck in votive candles. Candles everywhere say "Welcome."

CHRISTMAS CARD REGISTER

Time's precious during the holidays. Tuck a few Christmas cards in your purse and while you're waiting

...at the
doctor's office
or in between
trips picking
up kids,
address
them
and write
letters.

"You merry folk, be of good cheer; / For Christmas comes but once a year. / From open door you'll take no harm; / By winter if your hearts are warm"

THOMAS TUSSER

82

THE BEST christmas catalogs, SHOPS & COOKBOOKS

84

Make angels in the snow!

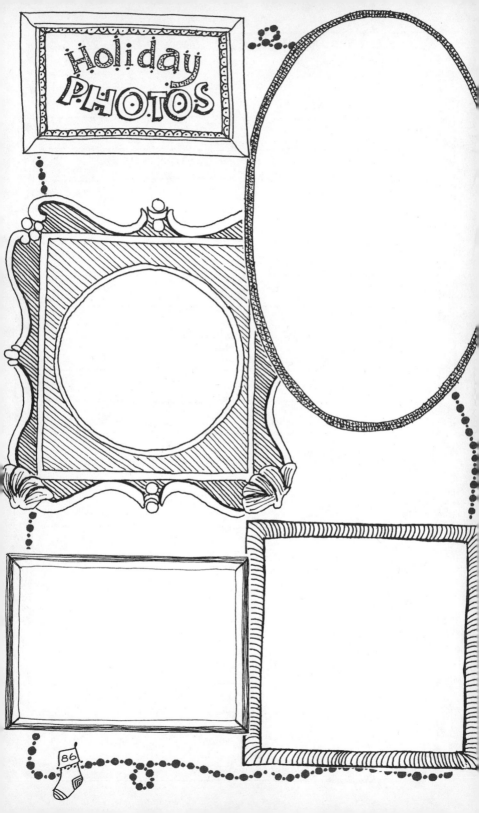

Holiday PHOTOS

86

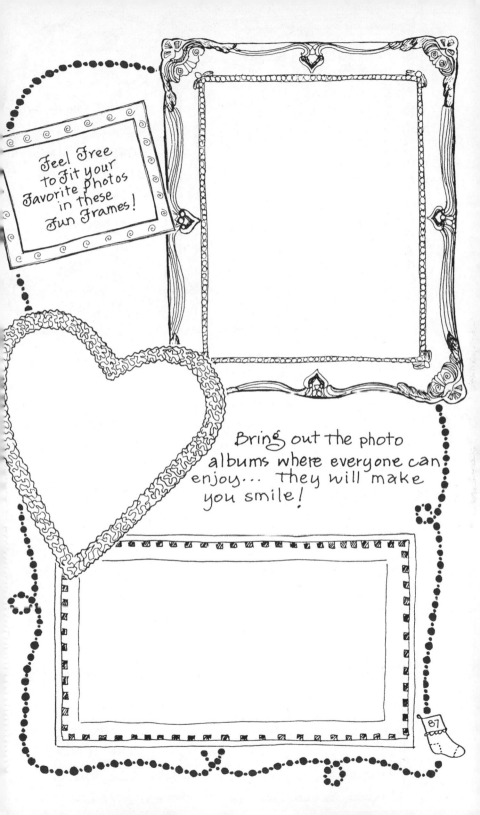

Feel Free to Fit your Favorite Photos in these Fun Frames!

Bring out the photo albums where everyone can enjoy... they will make you smile!

87

Keep camera
handy during
the holidays...
snap pictures
of kids with
cookie faces,
rosy cheeks
and happy
smiles!

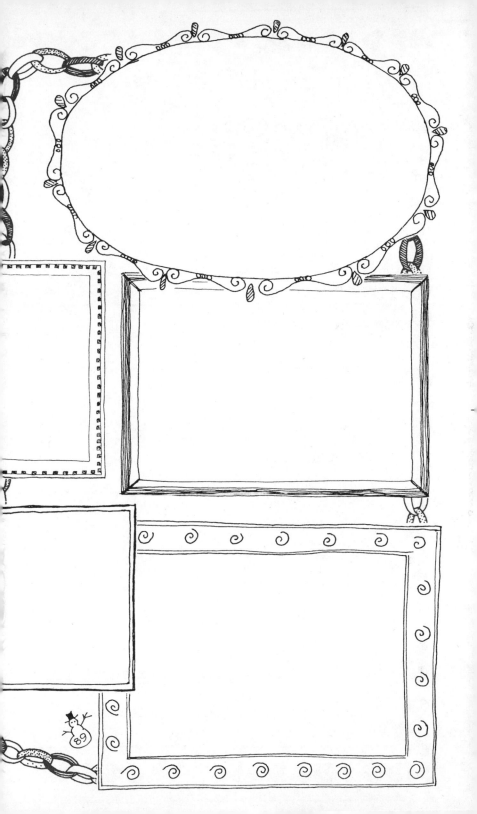

GUEST REGISTER

(Yule LOG. Get it?)

Fill an old sleigh, wagon, or bench with holiday packages. It's a great way to "Christmas up" the outside of your house.

Surprise someone with a kiss under the mistletoe!

93

We've cooked up a whole collection of Gooseberry Patch ® books!

Have a taste for more? Call us toll-free at
1-800-854-6673

We'll send you our latest catalog filled with snowmen, Santas, ornaments, candles, cookie cutters, gourmet goodies, salt-glazed pottery collectibles and MORE...including our best-selling cookbooks!

Phone us:
00·854·6673

Fax us:
1·740·363·7225

Visit our website:
www.gooseberrypatch.com

Send us your favorite recipe!

and the memory that makes it special for you! * We're putting together a brand new **Gooseberry Patch** cookbook, and you're invited to participate. If we select your recipe, your name will appear right along with it...and you'll receive a FREE copy of the book! Mail to:

Vickie & Jo Ann
Gooseberry Patch, Dept. BOOK
P.O. Box 190
Delaware, Ohio 43015

*Please help us by including the number of servings and all other necessary information!